Own Sweet Time

Caroline Clark live
Russian translator a
published a poetry
Editions), and *Sove*
stories accompanying photographs taken by her Russian
husband in his home town of Zhukovsky in the 1980s.

Own Sweet Time

A Diagnosis and Notes

Caroline Clark

First published in Great Britain in 2022
by CB editions
146 Percy Road London W12 9QL
www.cbeditions.com

Cover: drawing by the author, 2016

Printed in England by Imprint Digital, Exeter

ISBN 978-1-909585-49-2

Own Sweet Time

Conversation between Caroline, her husband
Andrei, and a consultant oncologist, whose
permission has been given to include this transcript.
March 2018.

. . . at last, we'll have ox-eye daisies. And peonies, foxgloves and hopefully the sweet-pea will be stronger. The beech leaves are still soft, but only a few days more and they'll be tougher, adult. Young and tender. Adult and tougher. But the wounds from when you were young weaken you as an adult. Examine, notice, consider these weaknesses. Faultlines. Questions.

. . . well yet, so I get to help him. I put my arm around his smooth water skin. He hasn't been tainted yet by the unhappiness. Oblivious or innocent, we all want him around. Tenderness for my younger brother.

. . . husband, who's Russian, doesn't understand why I should feel guilty about whether I go on a Sunday or not. He has learnt his Orthodox religion from scratch, reading everything and not having any guilt about how he should perform his belief. He is free to explore his faith.

. . . at° all? Any cancers run in the family?

No, no.

No? Um, any allergies to anything?

No.

Any, you've not had any surgery, anything like that?

No.

Ok. So generally just very fit and well.°

Mm-h

And, um, your periods still regular?

Yeah.

When was your last one?

It started on the 24th –

of February –

Yeah.

Ok. And you live with your husband° at home –

And two girls.

And how old are they? Sorry. Sorry. I'm sorry.

[Andrei] *Three and seven.*

. . . I pull. A satisfying click-release. The wet end with the follicle. I touch it to my lips. Discard. Repeat. One day I'll stop.

. . . we were terrified too. If it was like this now, what would it be like when she is a teenager? What problems will she have then? How will she cope as an adult?

Three and seven.

[Andrei] *Yeah.*

[*pause*]

It's always hardest when we talk about the kids. We are talking about curing you. This is all about curing you, you know. So –

[*whisper*] *I° just want to know the worst.*

Sorry?

Can you please tell me the worst?

Well, we° don't have all of the information yet. We got the, er, biopsy results. And yes they confirm what we thought. So, there is cancer there in the breast.

Right.

And, er, in both the biopsies they took in the breast and also the biopsy that they took from under the arm. So we know the cancer has spread to the lymph node area.

That's what I thought.

Um, we need to do some more scans.

Mm-hu

So I've requested a CT scan. And that will scan you from here to here. And it will look at your vital organs. So I can look at your lungs, your bones, your lymph nodes. It's unlikely, it's very unlikely that it's there, but we have to check. And obviously CTs can't pick up microscopic disease, but that's why

. . . first poem here. It's a good climbing tree and I can touch the roof of the house. If I could fly / up to the sky / past the moon / until mid-noon / past the stars and Mars / then down, down, down to the cars / but I can't fly up to the sky.

. . . are you still ours mummy? she asks. In the second cycle, it's clear I'm not going to have an easy time of it. I've been unable to get out of bed for a week. It's that personal pronoun *ours* that gets me. Still so little, she can't speak properly. But big enough to know what she wants to say, to get all the information. Have I become someone else to them?

. . . sometimes at closing time we'd crawl around on the carpet behind the counter picking up pins, price tags, things that had been dropped. Once I found a ring down there.

. . . you're a writer then.

. . . female in her mother's line to try to live the way she wants to and not sacrifice everything for her children but enjoy the journey with them.

you're here to see us first,° rather than the surgeons. Because what we'd like to do is give you some treatment that goes through the whole body. You are° young and, this is, you know, more extensive that we'd hoped it would be, so we want to try and get some good treatment in quite quickly.

How long do you think I've had it for?

It's really hard to tell. Um, it's unlikely to have been there for years, but probably months. You know, we just don't know about the natural history. A lot of patients ask that question, but we really have no idea.

You don't know how long it takes to get to this stage?

No. We know that in general that breast cancer doesn't grow in days, or really even in weeks. It takes months, and sometimes° years to grow. But usually the ones that grow over years are the grade one cancers, rather than grade two, grade three. And your cancer, as far as we know from the biopsy is a grade two. So the grades are – if you look at the cancer under the microscope – how similar do they look to your breast tissue. Um, grade three is the most aggressive and looks very dissimilar, and grade one looks most like breast tissue and is the least aggressive. So you're° grade two and you're sort of somewhere in that spectrum in between. The other things that we check for on the biopsies is what your cancer is sensitive to. So yours is sensitive to oestrogen, which is the female° sex hormone, that keeps your periods, etcetera, so it's sensitive to that –

Which means?

Erm, it means that it's a good thing, because it means we

. . . cells rejuvenate, and then some.

. . . gone, what I wanted to say.

. . . from my handwriting whether I'll have anything worthwhile
to say. Any minute now.

. . . thing I do has been so tied up with my sense of worth,
ability to earn and personal survival. Most lethal of all was when
I tried to connect making money with it. I almost died.

. . . want to let mum go alone. Impending boredom, but duty.
We kneel, hoping for Eucharistic prayer number two – the
shortest one. We follow the text with our fingers, urging
it forward. But there is the lightness on leaving the church,
skipping down the hill homewards. A serenity from having been
there. A promise come good.

have a good target. Um, we can give you anti-oestrogen therapy for up to ten years to try and keep this all away.

Does that mean that oestrogen is causing it?

Oestrogen can drive it.

Mm-h

Doesn't necessarily mean it's the cause. The cause might just have been one or two actual body cells° just gone awry. But then the exposure to the oestrogen has driven it most likely to grow and possibly to spread to the lymph node. So one of the aims of our treatment is to reduce your oestrogen. So it's sensitive to oestrogen, it's also sensitive to a drug called Herceptin. So, it's HER-2 sensitive – that's what we call this type of cancer. And about ten or fifteen years ago that would have been a bad sign, and it explains a little bit why it's gone° from° the breast into the lymph node area of the body. Because those cancers can behave a bit more aggressively than we would normally expect them to. But now we have very, very good HER-2 targeted drugs, and they are antibodies – they are not as toxic as chemotherapy. You do need to be given some chemotherapy to start off with, but again, we're going to continue these antibodies for a year, and that's a good thing.° The longer we can give you targeted treatments the better. Because if even one cell has escaped, we want to try and get everything. So that's why you're here today, is because we want to discuss the type of treatments we give you. First that and then we do the surgery because we want° to make sure it gets through the whole body and then treats everything.

. . . just stop this behaviour, it won't help thinking about it as something that should be stopped. There are trichotillomania websites. There's one that runs a paid course over a month or so. I haven't done this yet. I've been hair-pulling for almost thirty years.

. . . swelling and contracting slightly. Lymphy is as lymphy does. I start to listen to my body. Is this too much? I get the answer.

. . . you've got to be willing to get down on your knees and play with them.

Mm-h

Ok? So it's sensitive to oestrogen, it's sensitive to HER-2. We'll talk about what that means in terms of –

Her?

HER-2 is the Herceptin receptor. And, er, as far as we know – we've just° taken a biopsy from one lymph node – we don't know exactly how many lymph nodes are involved. We won't know that until we do the staging surgery at the end of all the chemotherapy treatment.

How do you know during surgery?

Um, so, they take away your lymph nodes. So the plan is to do a mastectomy and all – clear all the lymph nodes once you've completed all your chemotherapy and antibody treatment.

And they can – lymph nodes can be removed?

Yes. Yeah, yes. Lymph nodes can be removed. There is a small risk that you'll get swelling° of the arm, what we call lymphoedema. But your lymph is quite a dynamic system, so the lymph channels will rework and find new ways to –

So I'll never have them there again, as such, is that right?

You° won't have lymph nodes grow back there, again. Yeah, they'll remove all the ones they can see, but you'll have lymph nodes in your neck, and this bit here. So –

I have been feeling twinges up here. Is it at all related?

Have you? Um, I'll examine you and see. Yeah. And our CT

. . . how much soothing should you give a child? As much as they can take? Can you over-indulge them? Spoil them — as the older generation would say. The new way: you can't ever show them too much love. At one point will they say, I'm good now, I can do it on my own? What if they have a hole that can never be filled? They'll take as much as they can get and never stop asking. Rethink the metaphor.

. . . anything else, just please not the *crying feeling*. The worst feeling you could imagine. Fear, anger, fury. All just before bed. We had put in hours of stroking, lullabies, trying various nightlights, stories, award charts, mood diagrams. It would subside then come back. Stronger than before. We'd try to stay calm. Call me if you need help we'd tell the other; often we'd shout and blame, knowing we'd done the wrong thing.

scan will tell. Because our scanning –

What's the CT scan? How° does that work? Is it one of those white tubes?

Yes, a white Polo machine –

With the loud noise?

Not the loud noise so much, that's the MRI. But the CT is very quiet –

Ok.

It's like a big round Polo –

Yeah, sure.

And you just slide into it. It x-rays all the way through and it takes basically cross-sectional imaging from your neck down to your pelvis. So it has very good images for lungs, liver, bones – it's pretty good as well actually, and lymph nodes you can see all those things on there. Like I said, it has a resolution of about half a centimetre, so we can't see anything° smaller than that, it doesn't really show up anything else. But it will be able to catch anything big that we can see bigger than that size.

So you can never find –

Microscopic –

No.

disease – you can never find microscopic disease. And quite often patients say to us, how do you know for sure that I'm clear. You know, you finish all the chemo, we don't do

. . . clear as it's always been. Possibilities flourish then expire, a skylight shut.

. . . *best things come from nowhere.*

. . . when someone doesn't think they're enough it's a hellhole to climb out of, sucking in all around.

. . . good at my desk, on the front doorstep with a sketchbook. When the house is empty I can have a room of my own. It's not all that when you have children under five. Then they start to leave you alone more. You can escape. When I was pregnant with my eldest daughter in Canada, a Canadian poet and editor suggested I read a novel about a female poet who couldn't cope with having a child and left. I think perhaps he was trying to warn me. But he didn't know you can't do this: everyone's experience is their very own to unravel in their own sweet time.

another scan if this one's clear,° because, this one's clear, then there's not much point doing another scan. But the microscopic disease we don't yet know how best° to measure. There is some research into bloods, but, you know, that's still in the research arena. What we will be able to do is, when° we do the surgery, we'll remove the breast and the lymph node tissue – we will be able to look at that under the microscope and see how much disease is left, if any. For some people, this treatment works so well, that actually, all of the disease disappears. And you can't even see it anymore when you take the tissue out.

Why would you – why do you take the tissue out then?

Erm.

Just to make sure?

Yeah. Yeah. We're doing some studies to see – if you get what we call a complete response on MRI scanning – do you really need to take the tissue out, or can you just do biopsies of the tumour bed and make sure there's nothing missing. But the gold standard is always looking at tissue under the microscope – that will always give you better resolution –

Mm-hm

than an MRI scan ever could. So, you know, it's just about whether our scan's good° enough to mimic what we see under the microscope.

Mm-h

So those are studies that are happening at the moment. Unfortunately – we do like to do breast-conserving surgery

. . . open honest face, like a pansy.

if we can, because, like I said this chemo combination works really well, and generally everything shrinks down really well, but the surgeons – we discussed your case yesterday – the surgeons feel that because there's at least two separate areas that they've biopsied, they're worried about the breast itself, and that there might be areas there –

Are you all right? Are you fainting?

Sorry –

[Andrei] *Er, no, I'm good.*

Do you want me to get some water?

[Andrei] *No, it's ok.*

Do you need a window open?° Are you ok?

[Andrei] *No, I'll be fine. It's just –*

Sorry.

Are you hot? Take it all.

[Andrei] *Yeah, it's – no, that's better.*

Yeah?

Put your head down.

I can open a window a little bit if that helps.

[Andrei] *No, that's, that's fine.*

Are you sure?

[Andrei] *Yeah.*

. . . me, promise me you won't die, promise me I won't die, promise me I won't get it. I wish you'd only told me you need to go to the doctor's to get special medicine. – Did I tell you too much?   Yes.

. . . too loud, too brash, that inner beast of ego saying laugh at me, yet still the softest creature ever sleeping, trust me, inside.

. . . a little about body-focused repetitive behaviour.

. . . then I lose the thing I love the most. Going out shopping with her and sitting in a cafe together. I worry about her but it's easier not to see her suffering. No comfort in others. I love my room, my wall.

Just stop me° if it's all too° much, you know.

[Andrei] *No, no, we need to know.*

You want to know everything, don't you. But if it's all –

[Andrei]*: Yeah, thank you.*

Um, so I was just saying that –

[Andrei] *Thank you.*

You sure? [*laughs*] I don't want to push all this stuff on you.

No, no no.

But, um, it's absolutely normal to feel like this. It's a° lot of information. And you've only just had the biopsies and the results. So it's a lot, isn't it?

Mm-h

Um, we always try and do breast-conserving surgery if we can.

Mm-h

But I think, for you, and the disease that's there, it would be safer to remove the breast.

Mm-h

Um, and then° we can always look at good reconstructive options later on, and we can talk to the surgeons about that. But at the moment, what we're trying to do it get you a really good cure and get you the safest operation and best treatments that we can give you.

. . . the utter obliviousness to others' feelings.

. . .alongside her until a cry – goldrush to the nerves. I am
sought after by my daughter, by time, life, not yet death.

. . . once I was on the train from Montreal to New York. The
border guards came on, asked me what I do, a formal question.
I floundered. – Well, I have a book coming out soon. – *Well,
you're a writer then.*

Yeah, sure. I'm fine with that.

Um, are you all right for me to go ahead and start talking about the chemo –

Yes, yes, we'd like to know how long it takes.

[Andrei] *Yes.*

Yes? So, basically, the° reason – the other reason we're seeing you first is because, so I mentioned this antibody called Herceptin, and that's given alongside° chemotherapy. And we usually give eighteen weeks of treatment when we give it before surgery –

Of the?

Of the chemo/antibody combination.

Eighteen weeks of –

Eighteen weeks. Yeah, so it's once° every three weeks.

Ah

So there's six cycles in total. And that whole process takes eighteen weeks.

Mm-m

And then you have the surgery –

Mm-m

And then the antibody continues for up to one year afterwards.

And what does – ok fine. I was just going to say, what does the

. . . so many things are stopping me. Maybe I am a clock.

. . . said that it's because she can feel I'm about to leave the room.

. . . to accustom myself to the 3 o'clock pick-up. Lose everything first then reassemble. Parts may be lost, discontinued, warped or misplaced till ten years have passed.

antibody do. It just fights whatever is –

Er, it does several things. So, it, um, highlights that cancer to your immune system –

Yeah.

So° that it can look at it and kill it off.

Yeah.

Um, it also causes the – the HER-2 is like a signalling receptor. So basically it sits on the top of your cancer cell, and it tells your cancer cell to grow, and it's just switched on all the time in your type of cancer.

Mm-h

So what the antibody does, is it – it kind of links onto the receptor and it switches it off.

Mmm-h

So it dulls it all down, and it stops it growing, which gives the chemo a good chance to work.

Mm-h

Um, and then, like I said,° once the chemo part is finished, the antibody continues to° highlight any other cancer cells that are left for your own immune system to eradicate.

Mm-h

We think that's the way it works. We're not a hundred per cent sure.

Mm-h

. . . everything is there, but there is a new layer of significance that distances you from what there was before. This distance is beautiful and inexorable, wide blue skies, hazy towards the horizon. You can see far. You exist in a new dimension where death is present, not future, not just a possibility. And as such you go around like before but find yourself on the other side. The fields and backroads, ways out of town on the way to a theme-park zoo where we went to while away the two-week wait are flavoured like that now. It's a taste you never lose, though it fades.

. . . after you've been there a while you won't know any different.

. . . nice to have a room you don't go into very often.

. . . sit in the side aisles for those likely to disrupt. Toddlers. There's a basket of children's books. The one with the flaps that are all torn off. We know it well. Suddenly she's off and does a lap of the church. Most smile and laugh.

Chemotherapy's very different. It's not targeted. So, the antibody's targeted, and it will only really go to the cancer itself because that produces lots of this HER-2. And the only other organ in your body that really produces a bit of HER-2 is the heart tissue. So we do an echo test before you start, which is an ultrasound scan of the heart, and we keep an eye on it once every four weeks or so. But you're young and fit; you don't have any history or risk of heart disease, blood pressure or cholesterol or anything. Erm, you're not a smoker, are you, so there shouldn't be any problem with your heart. Erm, so the antibody's very targeted. You get very few side effects from the antibody, but the chemo is a blunderbuss; it hits everything.° And that's why you're always a bit sicker when you're on chemo. But it is just for that first six weeks – six cycles, and then –

Do you feel it straight after° having it? And for the whole –

No. So we'll talk about how – that routine in a second. So those are the two things. The chemotherapy – six cycles, antibody for six cycles. Now, um, very recently. About a year ago, NICE° have just approved an extra antibody called Perjeta that we can give patients like you who are getting treatment before surgery. So you could have had this treatment either before or after your surgery – it wouldn't have made any difference to your surgery. The surgery's gonna be the same. And some people say, I just want to get it out, I don't want to sit° here with – for eighteen weeks with it in, having treatment, I just want to get it off and then have the chemo and Herceptin afterwards.

Mm-h

25

. . . before closing her eyes she'd sit up and erupt, 'I've got the crying feeling', and act like a child possessed. She was very articulate very early and I could tell this was a dreadful feeling. At four, at five, at six. Screaming, kicking out, slamming the doors, saying she wanted to die. If only she didn't have the crying feeling.

. . . my therapist told me to get a cork and stick a blunt needle in it, then when I feel the urge to pull I should touch my scalp with the needle. It can release similar hormones. I think it does help when I remember to have a cork with needle close by. I'm not quite there yet (you'll never be quite there). I stopped completely six months before I got married. I wanted my eyebrows.

. . . new way of making connections, of acknowledging the space inside us.

. . . time I thumped my fist down hard with all my strength on the duvet next to her. It wasn't the duvet but her stomach. She was winded. I was scared. Got her out of bed into mine. She tried to tell me it was ok. It wasn't. Something had to change. Slowly after the cancer year, I realised it wasn't her that needed changing, it was me. I needed to change. I needed to want to be there with her. How can you make yourself want something? You can't. Your only hope is to find inner peace.

And that's completely reasonable. And we can still discuss that if you want to. The reason I've counselled you – I'm counselling you to have it first is because you get a chance to have this extra antibody called Perjeta, which the NHS have only approved to use before° the surgery. So you're only allowed those six cycles.

You know what, I'm not going to make my° decision against what – your advice. So yeah.

I think, it, it, you know, we're looking at the best chances of curing you –

Yeah, yeah.

and we know that adding this antibody increases those chances –

Sure.

so then why would we, you know, do something different? So that's good news though. Because that's a new° drug that's only really just recently become available. So you're going to have two antibodies, not just one, and a combination of chemo drugs for that first eighteen weeks, surgery and then just one antibody to complete the year. Ok? Er, so I'll talk to you a bit more about the details of the chemo now. So chemo is a day case. You go in and come out the same day. You just have it as an infusion into the arm. Erm, if your veins aren't very good, we can put a PICC line in, which sits in here, and just the tail sticks out and it's there the whole time.° Have you problems with your veins, or – yeah?

. . . came from the plastic surgeon we consulted prior to the mastectomy to learn about possible reconstruction. He looked at me naked from the waist up and said, *I don't expect they looked like that twenty years ago.* I'm not sure how strong the emphasis was on the *that.* I'm sure I laughed and agreed. The chaperone didn't react, my husband behind the curtain doesn't remember hearing this.

. . . got worse through the Covid years. The pulling areas have started to grow back, six months ago was bad, I can tell. Touch, twist, twist, pull. I need to give myself a chance to start again. I need to start again. No, this thinking goes nowhere good. I'll get by. Some days are good, some days are bad.

. . . struggle between the part that thinks they owe me something and the part that thinks I don't deserve anything.

. . . take on assignments as a community interpreter. Each time I help someone through interpreting, I feel my sense of worth increase. I can now tell people who ask what I do, how I earn money. It's peanuts, but it's something. I love to help others, to funnel all my privilege of knowing how things work into their lack of understanding.

Erm, it's hard to say. I really haven't had much call to –

Many – given blood or anything like that?

I've been meaning to all this time and then I just, either I've been pregnant or breastfeeding –

No, of course, it's fine, yeah.

And then this came° up, so –

Yeah, of course, of course –

Um

so the chemo nurses are very good. We'll have a look and see. We don't use the veins up here, we use the ones down here actually –

Mm-h

and they're usually a bit better, so I think, um, your veins will be fine actually. I see you've got° a couple there. They can use either side, because we haven't done any surgery yet.

Mm-h

Do you know what, we might actually – I'm gonna refer you for a PICC line because I think that it will be easier. I think your veins will be fine for one or two cycles and then they'll struggle.° So I think it's just easier for them to have that line in.

Sure, sure.

And they can take° bloods from there, and they can do everything –

. . . is when you record your thoughts.

. . . used to have things I should do, things I needed to do, things I'd never do. Now all the doors and windows are open.

. . . sick with the past. Sickos.

. . . few months, half a year, a gradual, deeper understanding that people, humans, depend on, need others. We've built this world for each other. This is why stories. Why business. Why sport. Why education.

. . . side that my eldest daughter first drank from, watching her make her way up my torso to install herself there. I didn't have to do a thing.

Sure, sure.

and then you don't have any more of the needles. So we'll do a PICC line for you. Erm, and you – the day you have the chemo you don't really feel anything. On the day – you get very good anti-sickness. Our anti-sickness is° much better than it used° to be –

What's that? Special medication?

Special anti-sickness medication. Yeah, not just what you can buy over the counter –

Mm

specially for the type of chemo regimen that you're having. Um, and then you have the chemotherapy into the vein. Again, you won't feel very much on the day. And then you go home, and you might feel a little bit nauseous that evening, and you might feel a bit sick° the next few° days –

Mm-h

a bit groggy, a bit tired. Erm, a bit like you're hungover –

But are you playing that down a bit because I've just heard awful things, so –

Well, there's a whole –

Does it depend from person to person?

range, yeah, there's a whole range. I'm gonna give you the general experience. And you'll get a booklet of all the side° effects. I'm not going to go through them all with you –

Mm-h

. . . eat everything I was given, too much, such sadness. The gap between us and happiness.

. . . last of the Victorians, hell at an arm's length.

. . . get what they need in the strange new world they find themselves. Lithuanians, Latvians, Russians, Moldovans, Ukrainians – anyone who speaks Russian. The young pregnant woman – I give her my full attention and help her pregnancy run smoothly. The Ukrainian teenager suffering from anxiety – I give her my attention and ensure she leaves with concrete help.

because there's only so much, really, you know, you can take in.

Sure, sure.

Um, and some people are fine, you know some people come in and they say it wasn't a problem –

Are you physically sick?

No –

No –

not usually. It also depends on the type of chemo you have. So some people have different chemo to others and they have different side effects. But this regimen – this combination of chemotherapy is not one that's gonna make you feel very sick. But you will probably feel nauseous –

Mm-h

erm, and you'll probably be a bit off your food, erm, you'll have a metallic taste in your mouth. It doesn't really matter what you eat° in that first week. Just eat what you can. Because you won't fancy –

So the nausea can last° the day after –

Three or four days after. Yeah, and you get° anti-sickness to take every day –

Ok.

for those three or four days. And extra anti-sickness –

Ok.

. . . every time I've spoken to the priest I feel, *ah, so it's not like I thought, ah so they're not judging me for that.*

. . . rarely now selfishness. Guilt and suffering, yes.

. . . enough. And so we learned what kinds of things had a greater value.

. . . around sixteen I find hair pulling. I'll sit on the sofa and at the end of the evening there'll be a dark mass of hair on the floor beside me. I learn to gather it up quickly before others can see. I know my mum knows. Then at university in the toilets with a light overhead I realise parts of my scalp are showing through. Too visible. I move my picking site to the side or lower down towards the back of my head where the rest of my hair can cover the evidence. I move to my eyebrows; they can be pencilled back in. Sometimes my eyelashes, which I regret and wait for to regrow. I regret the eyebrows and eyelashes the most.

if it lasts any longer. Erm, like I said, you shouldn't really be vomiting with this chemo. If you are, just call up because we have other, more anti-sickness –

Mm-h

we can give you. But we just give the standard amount to start off with. Ok? I'm gonna still keep stopping every° now and then just to give you a moment to breathe, because you know it's a lot, it's a lot of information.

[Andrei] *So it will be one day, er –*

One day in, yeah. I'm going to carry on telling you about this. So it's three weeks. So three or four days of this just feeling just not very well, metallic taste like I said, tiredness as well. Erm then you start to feel a little bit better by the end of that third week – sorry by the end of that first week. And in the second week you're at risk of infection. And that is the most serious side effect of chemotherapy. So if you get an infection, erm, you can become very unwell very quickly. And we very rarely° have deaths with chemotherapy, but if we do it's because somebody developed an infection and didn't come in quickly enough.° If you come in – so what we always advise everybody to do is to have a thermometer at home, take your temperature if you feel at all unwell and just call us. You'll be given a phone number to call day or night and then if they say get yourself into hospital, get into hospital. In A&E they have to see you and treat you with intravenous antibiotics within one hour. We don't wait – hang around° for four hours.

Do you, erm, are you saying this happens in the second week?

. . . only at the end do you let go, return to what you know, yet, for a while at least, remain more flexible.

. . . infection: the need to say something. And it will out.

. . . chickenpox. A day off school. I like it. Watching TV. The Flumps and Pebble Mill. I have my pillow and duvet downstairs with me. A car draws up. My insides tense up. The man in the suit enters. All comfort goes. He has bought the Lucozade. It is his duty. He goes upstairs to be on his own. We relax.

. . . middle of June and nothing. The lines are down – dead communication, not sure when things will pick up again.

The risk of infection is only° really in the second week. That's when you have to look out for it. And it – this sort of life-threatening infection° happens in less than probably one in ten, less than one in ten patients, probably about two to three per cent risk. But you must be aware –

And is it like viral –

Yeah, yeah. So viruses not so much –

No.

it's generally actually bugs that live inside you already –

Ah

And because your immune system's compromised they grow. But if your kids are poorly, you know, not just the normal viruses, but a vomiting bug or, you know, things like measles, chickenpox° or all those things that can go round, then you've got to work out some way of trying to isolate yourself. Do you have a good support network of friends and family?

Yeah, I think so. My parents live in the same town as me.

Oh do they? So, ok, if you needed to be away or needed extra help –

Yeah, mm-h

then you could do that. And I like I said, it's not the whole three weeks, it's just that middle° week that you, that we worry. We will give you some injections to boost your immune system –

. . . day automaton

. . . find my right pen. This doesn't look good. I may as well stop. Any minute one of them will come and need something. It's ok to be needed, what do I need? Life teaches me what I need. I sometimes learn too late.

. . . nails. I sit cross-legged on the floor at assembly in primary school. I lean back on my hand, fingers bent so they can't see my bitten nails. This is too visible. I move to biting the insides of my cheeks, that's safe. Then to turning circles as if a thread is attached to me. If I turn a circle one way I have to undo the thread and turn the other way.

Mm-h

so that will help as well, keep the immune system a bit higher whilst you're going through the treatment. Also you can feel very tired and achey in that week as well –

Mm-h

So, one of the chemotherapy drugs can, can make your muscles and bones ache a bit like flu-like symptoms. You know, so you can feel a bit achey and tired. I would say just make sure you can get out the house every day,° because that, actually, that exercise, that walking around can really help. Third week you start to feel a bit better again. And then you start the process again.

Mm-h

So it's once every three weeks, that infusion. The side effects that are accumulative are not the nausea – that kind of stays the same. It's more the tiredness and the achiness –

Mm-h

Er, some people also find° that their nails can get a bit sore, and their nails start to lift. Erm, one thing we've advised is to paint your nails° a dark colour. Sometimes that can help, because it's the light interacting with the nail bed –

Ah

that causes them to become sore and lift up. Erm, you can also get some pins and needles and numbness in your hands and feet, so that's important to let us know, because we might want to decrease some of the doses of your chemo-

. . . don't know how to say it other than to simply say it: I don't ever want you to be sad about your weight. I'm saying this before you even think of it, before it's even a thing and I don't know if I'll ruin it by saying it now.

. . . *what's the future?* – Something that's going to happen. And the past is something that has happened. – *In the past I fell off the climbing frame.* Yes.

. . . like approval. I like to do the right thing. At twelve I am given a very dangerous task at school: we are to write an essay titled 'A Portrait of Myself'. I realise that word, that thing I've always known, is real – the self. I love writing that essay. It's lyrical, about autumn and nature and full of longing. Mostly, it's about my love of God. I still go to church when told, find it boring, then I come home. The other thing, self, is expanding. The first time it happened was when I was standing on the front step. I caught sight of my hand, examined it and realised this was me. I am me. Self.

. . . who will beg you not to read what lies ahead. Lispector in her last breath – go away you who seek to make this real. *The Cloud of Unknowing* – turn away your eyes and please do not think that these pages are for you.

therapy. You don't° have to call us and let us know as soon as it happens, but, you know, we'll see you every three weeks, so when you come back to see either myself or the chemo nurse, or one of the breast team, then let us know what your side effects are. And the tiredness is cumulative, so probably in the first cycle, in the first couple of cycles, you might not feel too tired in that third week, but as you get through to 3, 4, 5 and 6, you're gonna start to feel more tired. And that's expected. It's fine, you know, just listen to your body. You will recover afterwards, but just listen to your body whilst you're going through that. Hair loss is inevitable really with this combination. With some drugs you can, you can avoid it. Erm, and if it's important you can try the cold cap. It does work for about a third –

What's° that?

Erm, so that's like° a shower cap you wear over your head –

Mm

And it pumps ice-cold water through. And you wear it for about half an hour before, during the treatment, and half an hour afterwards. And it probably saves the hair in about a third to a half of our patients.

Is that something you arrange for privately?

No, no, no, no, no. So, it's just an option. You don't have to decide today. Erm, what will happen, is – I give you all the information. You go away and read it all, and then just have time for it to sink in. Then you come back and speak to the chemo nurses, who° will go through everything with you again. And so that's when they'll offer you – whether you

. . . where the Downs continue. A nodal town. Along the Offham road, my favourite direction out of Lewes, into the beech-lined back roads that glow in the autumn. When I lived abroad I always dreamt I was travelling along that road towards my home town, my final destination, but I'd never quite make it.

. . . either I go on this way or I seek help. I need help to stop. I can't do it alone.

. . . yes, the eternal yes.

. . . need to make money. This thing doesn't bring me money. I need to make money. This thing doesn't bring me money. I will stop doing this thing. The cancer comes. My friend writes me letters. She says that whatever I do, I must write. It's time to accept the thing I do. To let it be. It can come and go, it doesn't need to make me money. It's time to get serious. I've known this all along. It's time to accept it. I pray and ask for help, to be shown a way forward.

want to try the cold cap or not. And they'll arrange it for you at the chemo unit. And they give you a voucher for a wig as well. So, you can go off and arrange that. They show you around the unit, so you know where you're going and that sort of thing –

Is it here?

It's at the Country – Royal Sussex County Hospital. Or Princess Royal. Where° do you live, Caroline?

Lewes.

Er, so which is easier for you? Which would you rather?

Which is the best? [laughs]

Er, they're both the same. The units are the same, so I've just got to check that they can do the drugs at either.° Sometimes with your combination of drugs, you might be better off having it at the County because it's –

They're both the same –

Yeah, fine. Erm, so yes,° there is a carpark just opposite the, um, hospital there in the Macmillan – the Horizon Centre.

You're allowed to park there?

As a cancer patient

Oh, right.

you're allowed to park there. As a cancer patient you're allowed to park there. Erm, so they'll go through all the side effects with you again. We'll check your blood test before every cycle. We need° to make sure that your liver functions

43

. . . on purpose, she knows what she's doing.

. . . I'll unpick what I know and what I don't know. I'll learn about Catholicism and see if it's for me, or if I'm for it.

. . . March 2019 I cleared a month. I said I wouldn't plan to come downstairs and have time to myself in the evening, I would be prepared to be there with her. I would simply do this. I wouldn't try to extract myself from her clutches, be rid of her presence. I would be with her. We had seen a therapist twice about her bedtimes, which had certainly got the ball rolling. Such simple, monumental revelations.

– is working well because the chemo can affect that a little bit, but that's usually fine. The kidney function we check, erm, we check your blood count to make sure your immune system has recovered again before we start the next round. So it'll be six rounds.

When will it start?

So probably in about two weeks. Erm, I've already requested the CT scan. So I'll request the echo test that I mentioned –

Mm-h

that you need to have done. Erm, and then we like to start within two to three weeks – it depends on° scheduling, you know. So I'll° refer you in and then you'll get contacted by the chemo unit directly.

So what's eighteen weeks from – so it lasts eighteen weeks?

Eighteen weeks. So it's twenty weeks from now. So roughly by the time you would get to your surgery. So we are currently, let's see, in March,° 1, 2, 3, 4, 5, 6, 7, 8, 9, 10, 11, 12, 13, 14, 15, 16, 17, 18, 19, 20 – erm, mid July, mid to end of July.

Is the end of chemo or surgery?

Yeah, end of chemo. And then surgery's usually, erm, so usually, surgery would be in that sort of first week of August.

Mmm-m. And can you rate my chances at the moment? Have you seen similar cases before, or –

Yeah, yeah, yeah, yeah.

or are they all very different?

. . . young. This inability. Until I do. This lack of self-esteem, confidence. This stuckness for want of approval. It's time to find a way forward.

. . . chance to do as I please? If tired – sleep, if low – languish? No more than that.

. . . for the moment, but sometimes I wonder: who or how would I be if there was a basic income?

No, um, so we, we've, we unfortunately treat a lot of young°
women, erm, and I think that we don't have all the information. Like I said –

Yeah.

we don't have the CT scan results, but assuming that that is
clear, this is all to try and cure you.

Mm-h

You know, and you have a very, you have an 80 per cent
chance° of responding well to this treatment.

Mm-h

And, you know, that's, very basically – you're gonna respond.

Mm-h

Erm, and the question just is to make sure there's nothing
else elsewhere.

Mm

Er, and then when we get the surgical specimen, when we
remove the lymph nodes, we can get a slightly better idea of
– so usually, what happens is – if there was any cancer in the
lymph nodes we see scarring.

Mm

And we'll get a better idea of how much disease there was
than when we started. Because we don't know that for° sure
yet.

Mm-h

. . . say, *ça fait du bien.* It means so much more in Quebec. It says, you're out of the woods, and good, it does you good.

. . . way of concentrating, being stressed and tired too. But it's so connected to my sense of self-worth. I feel devalued when I do it; this is the real damage. I think, *when it all grows back, I'll be better, things will be better, I'll be able to start again, better.* So, it's not ok. I told my husband and eldest daughter, *if you see me pulling, tell me to stop.* But I'm so good at hiding it, they hardly ever see. What goes on inside me is my own. No one else can know.

And then we've got some algorithms we can put that into, and we can give you some percentages if that's what you're interested –

Mm-h

in looking at, so we can do that. Erm, but what I'd say° is first, the most important thing is to try and get a really good response and shrinkage –

And will you check this side as well now?

Yes, yeah. I'll examine you clinically, yeah.

But did you have a mammogram of this side?

The mammograms aren't very good at –

Not that good –

going all the way° up into, under your arm. So it's almost better just to examine you –

Ok.

And then, erm, because it's quite easy to feel lymph nodes –

Oh right, ok.

if they are there, er, under the arm. And, um, if it's in the tail of the breast, then we can ask the radiologist if the mammogram got all the way around that side. Um, but yeah.

But the CT scan will, that also cover that –

The CT won't – is not good at breast, not good at breast. It's good at looking at lymph nodes –

. . . it doesn't come easily, nor should it.

. . . that night I thought how sad it was to have had this final judgement made on my breasts. Of course, he spends a lot of his time operating on women who have chosen to have procedures because they want to improve how they look. He was just being objective. But he forgot, I wasn't there because I was unhappy with how I look.

. . . spreads through the family. So you deal with some's lack, inability. Someone's dead-zone blocking you, ceasing you up.

Oh, ok.

but not so much the breast.

So the CT scan is for organs –

Yeah.

How far will it° go?

To your pelvis. From your neck to your pelvis.

So it covers ovaries?

Yes. But not very well.

Mm

So yes, they can be seen. Erm, ovaries, if you're worried about them – it's more an MRI that° you need. Are you worried about your –?

No.

No?

I'm just wondering what the – I'm wondering how it can – can it communicate to other parts of the body, this kind of cancer?

Yeah, so th– So any type of cancer can – the way it spreads° is twofold: so either directly, so just out through tissue –

Yeah.

or, actually threefold – directly, er, through lymph channels or through blood vessels.

Mm-hmm

. . . and you'll be a man, my son.

. . . year ago today the pound of flesh was taken. In this way, I can't help thinking, have I paid?

. . . up about 7.30 after being out on the pavement, playing with a neighbour. Good mood, gets washed quickly. Listens to the book calmly. In the bedroom asks me to tell her two stories from my childhood. I do and say then I'll leave and come back after ten minutes to check her. I sit for a few minutes. She's sitting up, saying can't sleep. I say gently that she needs to be lying down with still arms (*sleep can't find you if you're moving around*). We agree I can leave. 8.15 p.m. After a few minutes we hear her come out to look at the heavy rain. Goes back to bed herself. Soon after she comes out again. A goes up to check and stays there and he tells her two childhood stories and hugs her. Good mood throughout, but no effort to lie still. Finally asleep 8.50 with A there. No crying feeling.

. . . sensitive child. I was highly sensitive. I was surrounded by similar people but, I was told, only 25 per cent of people are like this. Not everyone is like this. Take my go-to-sleep-at-the-flick-of-a-switch second daughter. Things slowly but very surely changed. She got older too and the fears subside.

So there's three different ways of it getting through. Which is why the lymph nodes are important.

Yeah.

But even if they are clear, for some people it's still spread outside of the lymph node area. So we won't – what we really want, is, you know, before we start thinking about any sort of longterm things, we just want to check the scans and things, ok?

Mm-hm. All right.

We're looking to cure you. That is the aim. You've got a good chance of getting cured. Ok?

Ok. And° then after everything's been done, the operation and everything –

Mm-h

do you regularly check, or do you just assume I'm clear –

Yes, so we do mammograms every for, five year° – oh, up until fifty, so for the next, er, ten years. Obviously we get you to self-examine.

Mm-hm

Um, you have antibodies to complete a whole year, and then you'll have hormone therapy, so probably Tamoxifen to continue for, um, up° to ten years –

Mm-hm

And that's fighting the oestrogen-sensitive° side of the cancer. So you're not just stopping treatment after the surgery.

. . . out an ordinance survey map. I like to see him looking at maps, folding, tracing a line with his finger, finding the right spot. There, he's found the ford we used to go to when I was little. A ford is a stream or river that crosses a road. A ford is a place he liked taking us. A ford is a place he knows how to get to. A ford is a place we are looked after at. He can do maps. He gives me a spare copy of the Ashdown Forest map. I find the ford and go there with my children. I wish I could ask him to come along. Maybe next time.

. . . whether punishment is necessary.

. . . five-leaf clover and a favourite saint.

Um, there may well be some radiotherapy depending on how much cancer there was. But I'm just giving you that first part, and then as we get closer to the end we can discuss what happens –

Ok.

after that. And then when we get the surgical results we can discuss, you know, what we need to do after that.

Mm-h

So it's sort of more one step at a time, but we are gonna be able to treat you with some sort of targeted treatment for up to ten years, which is a good thing.

And not any longer?

Well, by then, we'll have some data out° for studies that we're looking at, erm, using these hormone treatments for fifteen, twenty years.

Mm-hm

So by then we'll have that information as to whether° it – so what we know is even when you stop your hormone treatment it still protects you for another five,° ten years probably. So, um, the question is, you know, do you need to keep going, or do you stop. We'll know that information –

So, if oestrogen is a bit of a problem –

Yes.

is it worth removing the other breast as well? Or, that's not –

Um, no, the risk of your cancer is now not from the other

. . . help out there until you actually do something, act. I did need help for many years and things only got much better when I said enough. The enough moment took years to come.

. . . feel. That wide new space of truth-telling. Is this what writing is? Putting down the truth?

. . . know there are parents who don't play for ten minutes a day with their kids? Just think.

. . . in 2021 if she has an echo of this old crying feeling I say, come on then, we go downstairs and see the hamster or the dog. She talks to the dog and I do the voice – always American. Everything changes, the great shift in mood happens and we go back upstairs happier. The old me would never had suggested she come out of her bedroom, to make, what would have felt, a step backwards away from the great goal of her being unconscious and me being free.

breast. It's from this cancer –

Ok.

So, so removing that won't help.° Erm, but yes, we need to reduce the oestrogen levels as much as possible. So the other question is gonna be: should we make you post-menopausal.

Mm-hm

Um, the chemo might do that. The chemo might stop your ovaries working.

Mm-hm

And you might feel° that you're menopausal whilst you're going through the chemotherapy. For some women their periods come back afterwards, but not necessarily all –

Mm

so in your mid thir– in your early to mid-thirties you probably would expect your period to come back maybe, but in your late thirties to forties, probably not –

Hm-mm

Um, have you completed your family?

Yes, yes.

Yes, ok, so, yeah, you wouldn't – you know,° I think your periods probably wouldn't come back –

Mm-hm

and in° that case, er, that's a good thing from the cancer point of view –

. . . talk but a kind of anti-talk, like one who doesn't believe in relationships, living as if to say with each interaction, *and let that be the end of it.*

. . . today I go with the flow. Wherever they place themselves I go elsewhere. But I keep at heart the plan to write. This is my first summer in eight years where I can, at the weekend, gather thoughts to myself, sit and read in places they don't tend to go. The little one is four, the big one eight.

. . . message that you were not really a person. But your sense of self will say otherwise.

. . . look back, each one sending us further into the unassailable past.

Mm-h

but we would then need to think about protective things like bone health and cardiovascular health –

Mmm

because that's what oestrogen is important for in women –

Mmm

is keeping your bones strong and healthy, and keeping the heart functioning.

Mm-hmm

Ok. We – lots of time to talk° about all those things. Right?

My main question really today° is – what to tell my children.

Well, we're gonna do – we're gonna cure you. That's, you know, that's the message° you've got to take home. Of course, we can't cure everybody, but we've got to look° at this positively. You're gonna have a year where you're in hospital, or having appointments, or having treatments. You know, the next year's gonna be quite hard but, by the end of 2018, there's gonna be a light there. You're gonna have got through all your treatment and, fingers crossed, getting back to normal.

My concerns are very short-term, like today –

Yeah.

[pause] either I let them see me, or I just stay away –

They're three and seven, did you say?

. . . because my mother is. Italian, Portuguese line. But also my father. His Italian mother lives here in our town. She sings loudly and out-of-key. I go to Catholic school. We pray there, not too much. I go to Catholic secondary school. There I learn that most people in this country aren't Catholic and that non-Catholics come to the school too and don't have to go to all the masses we go to. It's not an issue. Who's Catholic and who isn't. My belief in God doesn't depend on my being Catholic. We learn a little about the Bible. I know the main New Testament stories. But I don't know what it means to be Catholic in a way that is a system laid out for you. Is there a right and a wrong way to be a Catholic? The goodness is there and in me. I haven't learnt to to judge others. I can be Catholic like this.

. . . school. I knew when Mr Redfern, the supply teacher, got us to memorise the start of 'Maud'. I read it to my mum in the kitchen. 'Come into the garden, Maud, / For the black bat, night, has flown.' I composed a few poems but it all stopped at secondary school until I was seventeen.

. . . hard if you are then trying to imagine what judgements are being made. I learnt from a young age to see myself through the eyes of the hostile other. Can I do this a different way?

The seven-year-old is very scared of any kind of illness –

Yeah.

And I want to ask whether you advise I use the word 'cancer' or just – because° it means a lot to someone of that age –

Yeah, it can.

Especially as a mum recently died in our school° –

Mm, mmm, I'm sorry to hear that.

So –

I think, obviously you know your kids the best, but we have some very good literature. So, you know, Sharon can help you with that and show you all the literature that we can give to the kids as well. You know, what terms you use, you don't have to use the term 'cancer'. You can introduce it slowly to them, that actually you're going to start having some treatment and it's gonna to make you a bit poorly. And that, you know you're gonna experiment with hair a bit, but actually, you might have a wig, you might have hats. You know, it's just ways of trying to make it more – not so serious. Um, they're very young, aren't they? Seven and three. They're, so –

It's harder for the seven-year-old.

Yeah.

The three-year-old –

Yeah, it's hard° to – explain, isn't it? But we've got good literature, and Sharon can take you through that about how we, we –

. . . questions I'll never get any further with the thing that I do. Auto fiction? Essay of the self. I need to do this in fits and starts. Straight to the desk after drop-off. I used to get up in the silence of 5 a.m., write, then go back to bed.

. . . if you weren't enough without it, you'll never be enough with it.

. . . do you expect to be able to change at the turn of the calendar page?

. . . am a jeweller's daughter.

. . . self-denigration, an inner lack.

Ok.

Any other questions° at all?

Um, so right now you want me to go . . . for?

Well, first of all, do you mind if° I just finish asking you some questions? Is that all right?

Yes, fine.

So, um, so, we're just going back to the social history, so you – so obviously you live with your husband –

Yeah.

and then your kids are at home. Um, what do° you do? Are you working, or?

I, I, I, I'm more like a stay-at-home mum at the moment –

Yes.

I, I am° a translator as well. I'm a writer, but not at the moment really.

So, sort of self°-employed –

Yes.

Yeah? So, in terms of financial aid, because obviously, you know, going through this is, is, is a long, long time that you may or may not be working –

This is the main wage-earner, so –

Yeah?

Yes.

. . . we drive out into the country. There's a light covering of snow. We stay in the back seat as dad gets out and walks to the verge to collect some firewood. I tell my brother our father is never coming back. I want him to cry so that he'll let me hug him.

. . . worth, value, wealth, price, cost, payment, income, tax, property.

. . . again. I start to write on my wall in pencil – so as not to put anyone out too much. I'm not stopped. I get a green folder to put my pages into. I buy a special blank-paged book and write them out there too. The summer air is warm and inviting, and I am being beckoned out into it. The night sky is immense and star-filled. I feel my future, a distant me, in what I am doing.

. . . week everything changes. How quick we are to die.

. . . about making connections and communicating their needs. So simple. I am grateful for these windows of time where I can feel like a member of society.

. . . guess this is what we all do – decide to give up, yet carry on until we want to carry on.

And we, we° can talk about grants and things as well, because it's always worth° just applying to be honest –

Ok.

You know, even if it means that you can then get a taxi to the chemo unit. Or just those little things that build up and, you know, you might end up having to take days off work and it, it, it, I think it's worth exploring those options.

Mm-h

So again° Sharon can take you through those. Um, do you drink at all?

Sometimes.

How much would you say roughly?

What's –?

A glass of wine?

A half a beer is like –

A beer is a unit, yeah?

Maybe about two or three units a week.°

Oh right, no, not very much. And how about° smoking?

No.

No. And are you active? Do you exercise? What do you like to do? I guess° your kids keep you active.

I swim, but I recently, since autumn have been doing some more, different kind of, intense, like HIIT –

. . . sudden and irreversible the change was. I clung to my time alone like a wild animal. I clung. But it couldn't work out that way. Life needed other things from me. A new choreography taking into account the moves of others.

. . . back or I went back to pulling. When it was really bad I did have thoughts that getting cancer and losing all my hair would help. I'd have a fresh start. I did get cancer and lose all my hair but the pulling was still there when my hair grew back. I'm ok with it. I don't need to get a fresh start. I have tufts of hair growing back from my two most recent preferred sites, on both sides just above the ear. These short tufts are tempting. I buy hair grips to save them. But I don't destroy myself if I fail. It's one of those things. A human thing.

. . . wrong decision.

Interval, HIIT training?

Yeah. And I was almost wondering whether that can –

Yeah?

cause this.

No, er –

Like a sudden° change in what I was doing.

Er no. Um, so HIIT, HIIT training is not – so it's good, it – you know it can cause muscle sprains, that sort of thing, but, um, no exercise is linked at all to breast cancer.

Mm-hm

Um, and, there isn't even a biological rationale that you might say, you know, oh well –

Can stress cause?

that – there's some biological question about stress, erm, or significant events like deaths or divorces or moving house. You know, significant psychological events. Have you been through? Have you –

The last four years, we moved back° from Canada. We did have a big –

It's very stressful, yeah, so, that can, what that can do is probably it won't cause the cancer, but if you're kind of prone or, you know, there's something that's going slightly wrong,° it might just mean that your body's immune system is not at one hundred per cent –

. . . grow like never before. I started TM almost a year ago. I
have a proper contract. Each book sold makes me £1. Or I can
buy my books for half price and sell them myself for £5. It's
not about the money, but it's very much about the money. I'm
not giving books away for free this time, except to those in the
acknowledgements. It's symbolic, it's real, it's money.

. . . type of person and so I find anything communal hard. I balk
at church groups and classes. But when our first daughter was
born we didn't hesitate to have her baptised. This is where we
belong. We go into churches when she's one or two. Living in
Montreal, she likes going into those big impressive buildings.
Just before she's three we move back to my home town.
Taking her up to my old church gives us something to do on a
Sunday when we are both battling the unexpected difficulties of
carrying out our dream of 'moving back'. We do talk to people
but are not able to enter the fold. I don't think we know how.

Ok.

And that's, that's what is, kind of, you know, back there.

Can stress, mm, make the oestrogen levels higher, or is it the other way around? The oestrogen levels can –

No, stress is not related to oestrogen. Stress is related to other hormones –

Ok.

and other, um, factors. Yeah, yeah, yeah. I'd say, you know, looking at your history there isn't anything really that you've done that will have caused this to grow.°

Mm-h

Um, breast cancer is very common. It affects one in eight women, unfortunately. So, you know, it can happen. But, fingers crossed, we've caught it early, and so, you know the whole aim is to shrink it down, get it out, and then do everything we can as insurance policy to make sure it doesn't come back.

And is this now more of a risk for my daughters? Is it like a hereditary type° –

No, no it's not, as far as we know, it's not.

Mmm-hm

Um, so genetic testing within the NHS, er, we're only allowed to test women that are triple-negative. So – nega-tive for oestrogen, negative for HER-2, um under the age of sixty, or any kind of breast cancer but under the age of

. . . shoulds and the ought-tos seem to get in the way for me.

. . . ask if it's ok if I come as I am and start from there.

. . . things we didn't know we were living with.

. . . try to hear the sermon but off to the side it's hard to catch the words. We won't kneel here, but draw and whisper. Heads close, whisper, whisper. We go to light a candle by Mary. I manage a prayer. She will kneel and look picture-perfect pious for a moment.

thirty. There may be, um, some benefit to doing a genetic test outside of those ages, but we can't, we can't do that within the NHS. So, um, there are other, there are other tests that you could think about, and we can talk about that a little later on down the line.

Mm-h

Um, but, you know, you don't have a significant family history, so I don't think you need to worry about – that your kids will get it – just yet. Ok?

Ok.

Um, I think exercise is important.

Should° I keep doing what I've –

Not HIIT training.

[*both laugh*]

Because interval training is very hard. But that's why I ask° about activities, so –

Swimming.

Er, with the PICC line swimming's going to be difficult –

Ah

that's the only thing, because you can't submerge it. So you won't be able to swim. Um, but walking, cycling, jogging, any of those things,° you know, I just think it's really important to, to keep yourself moving and to try° and get out and do some things –

. . . you so easily loved and left that place.

. . . two friends get it when I tell them months later. Shocked. *Did you complain? He can't say things like that.*

. . . now is a system. A way ahead. What are you working on? An essay. Ok. An essay.

. . . season. The dog-rose has started to bloom, May 17th. I've planted hollyhocks along the side fence, with creeping thyme. The bluebells, late this year, are almost over.

So do you cover it for a shower? How do you –

Yeah.

Yeah.

So it's got a bandage round it anyway, you can put a plastic bag around it, you can get a sleeve, you know –

Ok.

and then. You° could even have a bath. It just has to be out. It just can't be submerged, that's the main thing.

Ok.

All right? We would advise you not to travel abroad or any-thing whilst you're on chemo. Mm, dental check-up. Pre-sumably your teeth are fine.

But not bother at the moment, you mean? Or do it –

Er, dental check-up if you haven't done one in the last year or two.°

Yeah, I have in the last – it was fine.

No issues, so you don't need to redo anything there. Um, and, flu jab – probably a bit too late in the season now.° I think they've probably stopped doing those now, because we're almost out of winter season.° So, that's all. So, we'll examine you, and then what you'll expect – I'll get you the written information. The chemo you know – we'll give you a call, or send you a letter with the appointment to come –

Mm-h

. . . give up doing the other thing, the main thing I do. It is who I am. Not a career or a job. This is the crux around which there is much sneering between writers. Perhaps there are different kinds of writers. There are those who can make a career out of it and work in those circumstances. There are those who can't do their work that way. But work doesn't always amount to remuneration. It's a story as old as time. Those in the latter category must write their own rules for how to get by, work it out, not give up. *Poetry is the thing that won't give in.*

. . . available facts purposely veiled, the absence of truth, and we were fumbling in the dark.

for the first information sessions. So you won't be having chemo that day, and then they'll give° you the dates to start.

Mm

All right?

So I can ask them any directly chemo-related questions?

Exactly. Exactly. And anything that's come up between now and then. Um, because I'm sure things will. And usually what I do is I see you again in about four, six weeks time.

And will I see specifically you?

Um, we can try –

Or –

yeah, so we can try and keep it the same, and then of course, if I'm –

Sure.

not available,° then there's someone. You know, there's a team of three or four –

Sure.

of us, so yeah. All right?

Mm-hm

Ok? So shall we pop next door?

Yeah.

I'm just going to stop the recording –

My endless gratitude to the NHS and in particular to the cancer team in the south-east of England.

As an afterword I'd like to say that if breast cancer touches your life in any way, please remember that every diagnosis and case is different. And I wish you all the very best.